Hello Friends!

Places I Know

Imagine That!

Oh, What Fun!

Let's Go Outside

What a Funny Animal!

IMAGINATION
An Odyssey Through Language

Imagine
That!

Gail Heald-Taylor
General Consultant, Language Arts

 HARCOURT BRACE JOVANOVICH, PUBLISHERS

Orlando   San Diego   Chicago   Dallas

Printed in the United States of America

ISBN 0-15-332804-5

Acknowledgments

For permission to reprint copyrighted material, grateful acknowledgment is made to the following sources:

Harper & Row, Publishers, Inc.: The Carrot Seed by Ruth Krauss, pictures by Crockett Johnson. Copyright 1945, 1973 by Ruth Krauss and Crockett Johnson.
Macmillan Publishing Company: From *Changes, Changes* by Pat Hutchins. Copyright © 1971 by Pat Hutchins.

Art Credits

Willi Baum: 36-45; Carolyn Bracken: 29-35; Kinuko Craft: 2-15; Pat Hutchins: 16-28; Crockett Johnson: 52-75; Christa Kieffer: 46-51

Unit Opener: Tom Vroman

Contents

The Three Bears   2
An English folk tale retold in pictures

Changes, Changes   16
From a story in pictures by Pat Hutchins

CONNECTIONS: Dress for the Weather (Health)   29

The Mitten   36
A Ukrainian folk tale retold in pictures

Five Little Pumpkins   46
A rhyme

The Carrot Seed   52
A story by Ruth Krauss

THE
THREE BEARS

An English folk tale retold in pictures by Kinuko Craft

This porridge is too hot.

Let us go for a walk. When we come back, our porridge will be ready to eat.

3

6

9

Somebody has been sitting
in my chair—
and has sat the bottom out!

Somebody has been lying
in my bed—
and here she is!

Changes, Changes

A story in pictures by Pat Hutchins

Connections

Dress for the Weather

What is today's weather?

What are you wearing?

Today is snowy.
Today is cold.

We dress for the weather.

Today is rainy.

Today is warm.

We dress for the weather.

Today is sunny.
Today is hot.

We dress for the weather.

The Mitten

A Ukrainian folk tale retold in pictures by Willi Baum

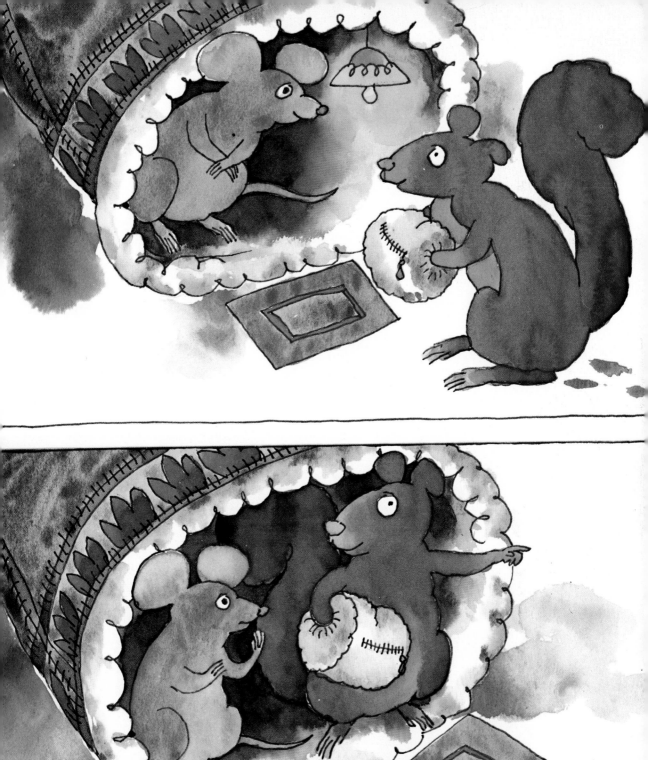

41

42

Five Little Pumpkins

A rhyme

Pictures by Christa Kieffer

Five little pumpkins
Sitting on a gate,
The first one said,
"Oh, my, it's getting late."

The second one said,
"There are witches in the air."
The third one said,
"But we don't care."

The fourth one said,
"Let's run and run and run."
The fifth one said,
"I'm ready for some fun."

"Oo-oo!" went the wind
And out went the light,
And the five little pumpkins
Rolled out of sight.